No Kidding, MERMAIDS ARE A JOKE!

The story of **THE LITTLE MERMAID**

as told by **THE PRINCE**

written by **Nancy Loewen**

illustrated by **Amit Tayal**

Raintree is an imprint of Capstone Global Library Limited, a company incorporated in England and Wales having its registered office at 7 Pilgrim Street, London, EC4V 6LB – Registered company number: 6695582

www.raintreepublishers.co.uk
myorders@raintreepublishers.co.uk

Text © Capstone Global Library Limited 2014
First published by Picture Window Books in 2014
First published in the United Kingdom in paperback in 2014

Edited by Jill Kalz, Catherine Veitch and Clare Lewis
Designed by Lori Bye
Art Direction by: Nathan Gassman
Original illustrations © Picture Window Books 2014
Production by Victoria Fitzgerald
Originated by Capstone Global Library 2014
Printed and bound in China

ISBN 978 1 406 27984 9
18 17 16 15 14
10 9 8 7 6 5 4 3 2 1

British Library Cataloguing in Publication Data
A full catalogue record for this book is available from the British Library.

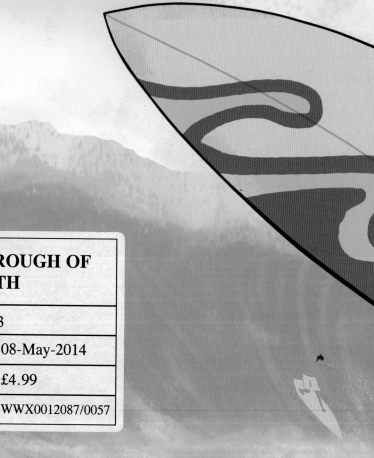

Are mermaids *real?*

A little while ago, I would have said NO WAY! Sea creatures with people faces and people arms but great big fish tails, instead of legs? That's nuts!

Then I met this girl...

3

My name is Prince Aleck. I'll admit, I'm sort of a practical joker. If you're looking for someone to put chilli powder in the toothpaste, or to glue coins to pavements, I'm your man.

But back to the girl... I found her on the shore one morning, just lying there. She was wiggling her toes as if she'd never seen them before.

She couldn't talk, but she drew pictures in the sand.
They were pretty wild.

She drew a merman king on a throne...

and a mean-looking sea witch...

and a mermaid drinking a potion...

and then she drew that same
mermaid girl, with human legs.

I was a little suspicious. Here's why:

Not long ago, I had a birthday party on my dad's ship.
That night a terrible storm came up, and the ship broke
apart. Everyone else got on a lifeboat, but the wind tossed
me into the water. I had this weird dream that someone
carried me through the water – someone with long, flowing
hair... and a tail.

Or was it a dream? I woke up the next morning on a distant beach. I didn't know how I'd got there.

Anyway, I made the mistake of telling my friends. They've been teasing me ever since. I can't go for a swim without someone throwing a doll in the water. I have to check my porridge for fish scales.

"Did Adam put you up to this?" I asked the girl. "Or Tommy? I bet it was Tommy."

She looked confused.

9

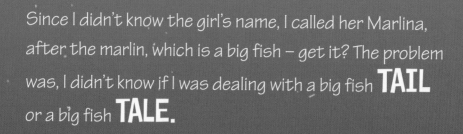

Since I didn't know the girl's name, I called her Marlina, after the marlin, which is a big fish – get it? The problem was, I didn't know if I was dealing with a big fish **TAIL** or a big fish **TALE.**

I liked her, though. Everyone liked Marlina. She could teach kids to swim and dive. She was great at dancing.

And she blew us away at the local dance contest.

Still, I couldn't shake the feeling that my friends were playing a trick on me. Especially when they said things like, "Your girlfriend's quite a catch" or "Aleck and Marlina, swimming in the sea,

K-I-S-S-I-N-G."

So I came up with a test.

Remember my birthday party? When I washed up on that beach? A girl from a nearby school had helped me out. She'd let me use her mobile to call home. Her name was Kim. I texted her.

KIM

Want 2 B on TV?
B famous?
Got a deal for U.

...

I took Kim along to royal events. I drew hearts around her name in the sand. I wrote letters to her on fancy paper and sealed them with a kiss.

I sighed a lot and got really good at making goo-goo eyes.

I still hung out with Marlina. But I made it clear we were just friends. "What a pal," I told her.

My parents were thrilled. "See, honey?" my mum said to my dad. "I told you he'd grow up sooner or later!"

This is what I expected to happen:

As soon as I was married, my friends, and Marlina, would admit that the mermaid thing was a joke. Then I would admit that I wasn't really married. The wedding was a fake! We'd have a good laugh, and life would go on as usual – or it would once my parents were over being mad.

This is what *actually* happened:

I got fake-married. My friends gave me a nose-shaped pencil sharpener and a case of chattering teeth as wedding gifts.

Marlina disappeared.

After the fake-wedding dance, for a second, I thought I saw Marlina's face bobbing in the sea, far away. But when I blinked and looked again, all I saw was some sea foam.

So, you tell me: Are mermaids real?
Don't tell anyone I said this, but my hunch is that they are.

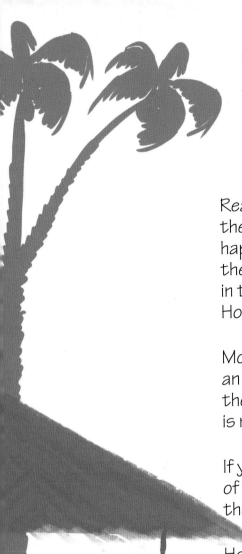

Think about it

Read a classic version of The Little Mermaid. Now look at the prince's version of the story. List some things that happened in the classic version that did not happen in the prince's version. Then list some things that happened in the prince's version that did not happen in the classic. How are the two stories different?

Most versions of The Little Mermaid tend to be told from an invisible narrator's point of view. This version is from the prince's point of view. Which point of view do you think is more honest? Why?

If you could be one of the main characters in this version of The Little Mermaid, who would you be, and why? One of the prince's friends? Kim?

How would other fairy tales change if they were told from another point of view? For example, how would Jack and the Beanstalk change if the giant was the narrator? What if the wolf in Little Red Riding Hood told that story? Write your own version of a classic fairy tale from a new point of view.

Glossary

character person, animal or creature in a story
narrator person who tells a story
point of view way of looking at something
version account of something from a certain point of view

Books in this series

978 1 406 27983 2

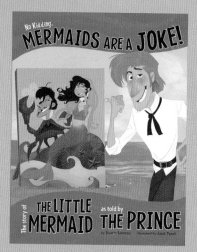

978 1 406 27984 9

978 1 406 27985 6

978 1 406 27986 3